قصص أنبياء عليهم السَّلام

Salih and Ibrahim

Abdul Rahman Rukaini

M
MACMILLAN PUBLISHERS

Bahasa Malay edition first published 1984.
Published by Macmillan Publishers (M) Sdn. Bhd. co-publication with
Pustaka Pertubuhan Kebajikan Islam Malaysia.

This edition first published 1985

Published by *Macmillan Publishers Ltd*
London and Basingstoke
*Associated companies and representatives in Accra,
Auckland, Delhi, Dublin, Gaborone, Hamburg, Harare,
Hong Kong, Kuala Lumpur, Lagos, Manzini, Melbourne,
Mexico City, Nairobi, New York, Singapore, Tokyo.*

ISBN 0−333−41418−7 (cased)
ISBN 0−333−40016−X(pbk)

Printed in Hong Kong

Adviser for text:
Ustaz Haji Abu Hassan Din al-Hafiz

Adviser for illustrations:
Abdul Aziz Ibrahim

Designer and artist:
Abdul Razak Abdullah.
(ERAL)

*Illustrations found in these series were not meant to
depict all the prophets, their companions, or anyone
concerned during that time. These illustrations were
only meant to picture the situation or episodes that
happened during that time. The Publisher has
consulted authorised personnel to seek their advice
regarding the contents and illustrations.*

British Library Cataloguing in Publication Data
Rukaini, Abdul Rahman
    Stories of the prophets of Islam.
    1. Prophets in the Koran—Biography—Juvenile
    literature
    I. Title
    297'.122'0922   BP134.P745

ISBN 0−333−41418−7 (cased)
ISBN 0−333−40016−X(pbk)

Preface

This volume tells the story of the prophets Salih and Ibrahim and how they struggled to bring the faith of Allah to the idol-worshippers of Samud and Babylon.

The stubbornness of the 'Ad people was inherited by the Samud people and they refuse to listen to the words of the prophet Salih. Even when the prophet gives them proof in the form of a miracle camel the people do not believe him and the camel is killed. It is Allah's will that the people of Samud, like the people of 'Ad, should perish.

The story of the prophet Ibrahim tells of how he bravely confronts the cruel King Namrud and how he is saved from the fire by the will of Allah.

The stories were carefully selected and creatively written to interest young readers.

Illustrations

Contents

The people of Samud

Between the bare, rocky mountains and the hot, dry, sandy desert there was a green, fertile river valley. This was where the people of 'Ad had lived. Allah had blessed them with rich earth and green fields. But the people of 'Ad had forgotten Allah, and prayed to their idols instead.

It was now many years since the destruction of the people of 'Ad. Camels and goats wandered in the plains again and birds sang in the trees. A new group of people had made their home in this beautiful land.

These people were members of the tribe of Samud, descended from the family of Nuh. For years they had wandered from place to place, until they found this lovely valley. Their leader, Janda', had gathered them beneath the shade of a leafy tree and said, 'We do not need to wander any more. This earth is rich. We shall make it our earth, the land of the people of Samud.'

And so they settled on the land. They farmed the fields and every year their crops increased. The people became wealthy. The leaders, men like Janda' and Zuab, became wealthiest of all. Soon they changed their humble tents for houses.

But then they became greedy.

They thought of nothing but their own wealth. The leaders took what belonged to the poorer people and forced them to work as slaves in their fields. Anyone who spoke against the leaders was treated with great cruelty. Soon no one dared do anything.

The people of Samud had forgotten what happened to the people of 'Ad. They, too, turned away from the truth and began to worship idols. The rich drank and held parties, and took any woman they wanted, while the poor slaved in the fields.

An old man stood outside his tent, thinking sadly about what had happened to his people. 'Why must they kneel to those idols?' he said to himself. 'The people of Samud are lost. They are cruel to their own people. I am old. I can do nothing to free the slaves.'

The scars on his body were a reminder of the time he had asked Zuab, the chief priest and keeper of the idols, 'Why must we worship lifeless idols?' Now he was too old and too weak to do anything more.

His grandson came out of the tent behind him. The little boy came running up and hugged him. As he held the boy in his arms, the old man could not hide the tears in his eyes.

'Are you crying, grandfather?' asked the child.

'No, I have dust in my eyes', replied the old man.

'Do not let this child suffer', he prayed in his heart. He could not protect the child from his own people. What would happen to him when he died? The old man had so many worries.

He let the boy go and looked up at the sky. Was he hoping that Allah would save his people? He prayed that someone would come, someone who would protect his grandson and show the people of Samud the right way to live.

The mission of the prophet Salih

The people of Samud continued to live a wicked life. They worshipped the idols and the rich used their power over the poor. Into this cruel world the prophet Salih was born. He belonged to the family of Samud.

As he grew up, the prophet watched with sadness the way his people lived. He hated what he saw and he worried about what would happen to his people. After many years, he decided to leave the lovely valley and go and live on his own in the desert. There he found peace to worship Allah and think about the wickedness of the people of Samud.

Allah knows all. He knew what
was happening in the land of Al-
Hijir where the people of Samud
lived and He heard the cries of the
poor. He chose the prophet Salih as
His messenger, to show the people
the right way to live.

So the prophet Salih left his lonely
home in the desert and went back to

live amongst the people of Samud. He had been sent by Allah and he knew he must find a way to teach his people to worship Allah and lead a good life.

Many of the people were pleased to see Salih again. They knew he was an honest young man and they liked him. He was sensible and they hoped the leaders would listen to him and stop quarrelling amongst themselves.

'Where has he been all this time?' was the question on everyone's lips. A crowd gathered round him.

Salih's thoughts were full of his message from Allah. He said aloud, 'Listen, my people.' The crowd fell silent.

'I have been sent to you, to ask you to worship the one true God, Allah', said the prophet.

The people listened to his words in amazement. Janda' and Zuab, the leaders of the people, listened particularly carefully. They realised what these words meant for them. They were powerful because they were the keepers of the idols. They would lose their power if the people changed their customs and beliefs as Salih asked.

They asked, 'Who has sent you, Salih?'

'Allah, my God has sent me to show the people the right way to live, to ask them to change their ways.'

Zuab laughed at him. 'Go back to the desert', he said. 'We don't believe you are a prophet. If a prophet was needed I would be chosen, not you.'

Salih was left alone. The people were afraid of Zuab and always did what he said. They laughed at Salih, too. They continued to worship the idols, drink wine and break Allah's laws. But Salih did not give up. He still spoke to the people and soon some of them began to understand his message. The rich still laughed at him but more and more ordinary people began to change their ways and worship Allah.

Soon the leaders began to worry. The number of Salih's followers was growing. They had to stop it. They tried to spread rumours about the prophet. They said he was mad. They said he wanted power and fame. They said he was lying. But still the ordinary people listened to him and stopped worshipping the idols. Then the leaders of the people of Samud began to punish those that followed Salih. But it was no good. Their faith in Allah was strong and they no longer feared Zuab and Janda'.

'We have faith in the prophet Salih', they said. 'He has shown us how stupid it is to worship idols. He has shown us the truth and the way of Allah.'

The leaders were desperate. They offered to share their power with Salih, they offered him money, but Salih ignored them.

They would have to think of another way to deal with the prophet.

بِسْمِ اللّهِ الرَّحْمَنِ الرَّحِيمِ

The miracle of the camel

It was a holiday and the people of Samud had come to pray to their idols. The leaders prayed for the success of their plan. They had tried many ways to stop the people believing the words of Salih, but everything had failed. Many of the ordinary people now followed Salih and the leaders were afraid they would lose their power over the people.

Now they had a plan, and they had invited Salih to their annual celebrations.

'We have prayed to our gods', said Janda' to Salih, in front of the crowd. 'Now you must pray to your God. If your prayers are answered, we will follow you. But if they aren't, then you must follow us.'

Calmly Salih explained to them that Islam was the religion of Allah and required complete faith. He and his followers would never pray to any idol but only to Allah. Their religion came from faith, not bargaining.

The prophet's calmness and confidence bothered Janda', but he tried to hide it.

'If you really are a messenger from Allah, you must prove it', said Janda'.

'What proof do you want?' asked Salih.

'Do you see that hill of stone?' said Janda', pointing in the direction of a hill nearby.

'Make a large camel come out of that hill, a red camel with huge black eyes and enough milk to feed all the people of this town', demanded Janda'. 'If you can do that, we will believe in your message.' Janda' was quite sure that the prophet would not be able to do it.

The prophet Salih was silent as he walked to the hill with Janda', Zuab and many of the people of Samud. He prayed silently to Allah to make the camel come from the hill.

Then, to the amazement of the people, the stone hill split open and a large camel stepped out of the crack. She walked calmly towards a well nearby.

The crowd were speechless. With Zuab and Janda' they stared at the camel. They couldn't believe their eyes. The prophet Salih knelt and gave thanks to Allah.

Janda' kept his promise. He turned to Salih and said, 'Yes, I believe you are the messenger of Allah. I believe in Allah the One God and in His prophet.

Many others did the same but still the majority of the people of Samud refused to believe. They would not even believe what they had seen with their own eyes.

'It's a trick, a trick!' they yelled. Zuab said Salih must have used magic.

'No', said Salih firmly. 'I am not a magician. I am the messenger of Allah. This is the camel which you asked for as proof.'

'O my people, worship Allah. There is no other God but He. He has sent this camel to show you this is true.' (*Al Quran, Surah al-Araf, verse 73*)

'Yes, yes, this is the truth', cried Salih's followers but their voices were drowned by the shouts of Zuab and the unbelievers.

The prophet Salih turned to them. 'Let the camel drink at this well', he said. 'Give it food and do not harm it. If you do try to hurt it something dreadful will happen to the people of Samud.'

The camel drank at the well, then allowed the people to milk her. There was more than enough milk for everyone.

Salih's followers gave thanks to Allah for the camel. The poor were delighted with the free milk and looked after the camel. But there were many people who took no notice of the prophet's words. They hated the camel. They complained that she frightened their sheep and goats.

'The camel is a nuisance', they said. 'Our animals are half-starved because of her.' They did not understand that Allah was testing

them. They did not understand that everything that happens is the will of Allah and that they must be patient.

Two women who hated the prophet Salih decided it was time to do something about the camel. One was an old woman and the other a young widow. They complained to everyone about the camel.

'Kill the beast!' they cried. But even some of the people who hated the animal were shocked by the words of the women. The camel was a nuisance to them but they remembered the words of the prophet Salih. They were frightened when they remembered his warning, and they were frightened because the camel was so big.

But Zuab and the other leaders of the people of Samud did not believe Salih's words. They agreed with the women and planned to kill the camel.

In a dream, Allah warned Salih that Zuab and his followers planned to kill the camel. Salih went to talk to them.

'Listen, my people', he said. 'Do not carry out this evil plan. If you do, you will suffer. Something dreadful will happen to the people of Samud. Pray to Allah for His love and forgiveness.' These were the words of the prophet Salih.

The plot

Zuab and his followers, Rabbab and Khabbab, refused to listen to the words of the prophet. They called a meeting to discuss ways of killing the camel. Zuab spoke to the crowd first. 'We must kill this camel!' he cried with hatred in his voice.

The people were frightened of him but one of them spoke up. 'What if someone disagrees with your plans?' the voice asked timidly.

Zuab's eyes flashed with anger. For a moment he was speechless as he looked at the faces of the crowd to see who had spoken. Before he could reply, the old woman, 'Unaizah, who hated the prophet Salih and wanted the animal killed, shouted out, 'Kill anyone who doesn't agree with us!'

'Yes, we will kill them,' said Zuab. But Rabbab was anxious to get back to the point of the meeting and quickly reminded them that the problem was how to kill the camel, not each other.

Everyone was silent, thinking of the prophet's words and how large the camel was. 'Unaizah was impatient. 'Are we too frightened to do anything because the camel is big and Salih told us not to hurt it?' she laughed at them. 'I will give a reward to the brave man who is chosen to do this important job for us.'

Sadqah, the young widow, stood up and said she would give a reward, too, and named Musadda' as the bravest man amongst them. He must be chosen for the job. 'Unaizah named Qudar. The two young men were surprised to hear their names but they stood up proudly. They were both strong and cruel and had killed before.

'Qudar, I will give you my daughter and all my most valuable things if you kill the camel', said 'Unaizah. Qudar was pleased with the reward and happily agreed. But Zuab and the people in the crowd felt such a difficult job needed two people.

'That is why I offered a reward too', said Sadqah. She walked up to Musadda' and in front of the crowd put her arms round his neck. 'If you kill the camel, you can have me and everything I own', she said. He was her own cousin, but she had no shame.

'For you, cousin, I would do anything', Musadda' replied.

Zuab and the other leaders of the people were delighted. The two women had solved their problem, and it had cost the leaders nothing! The crowd cheered Musadda' and Qudar and went happily back to their homes.

The next night Musadda' and Qudar left the town to carry out their task. They had persuaded some friends to come with them and carry their arrows and spears. As their friends cheered them, they felt important and had no time to worry about what might happen to them. But as they got nearer the hill where the camel was to be found, the cries of their friends died down. Soon the young men stopped and one spoke nervously, 'I don't want to go any further. The camel's very big', he said, looking down at the ground.

'Coward!' said Qudar, and he and Musadda' took the arrows and spears and walked forward alone.

The rain of arrows that hit the camel brought it to its knees. Qudar thrust his spear into the camel.

'We've done it! We've done it!' cried Qudar and Musadda' above the roar of the crowd.

The crowd rushed back in delight to find Salih and tell him he was wrong about the disaster. The camel was dead and nothing had happened.

The prophet was sad to hear the news. He told them, 'I warned you but you would not listen. For three days you will be free of Allah's anger but then He will punish you.' They laughed as he walked away.

Punishment

The people of Samud had gathered in front of their idols. They were celebrating their success in killing the camel. Qudar and Musadda' were enjoying themselves, surrounded by girls who wanted to gaze at the brave heroes. There was singing and dancing and plenty to eat and drink.

When the prophet Salih passed by, people turned to him, laughing at him. 'Where's your disaster now?' they shouted. 'We're waiting for Allah's anger.'

Calmly Salih replied, 'My people, why are you waiting for His anger. Why don't you ask for His forgiveness and blessing?'

'We don't need your God's blessing!' Qudar shouted after Salih. 'We have all we could possibly want.'

Qudar's friends were still laughing but Qudar felt angry. He wanted to kill Salih. His anger spread to the others and soon they had a plan. The leaders of the people of Samud were pleased to hear what Qudar, Musadda' and their friends planned to do. The camel was dead but they did not want Salih and his family to live either.

When it got dark, Qudar, Musadda' and the others hid behind

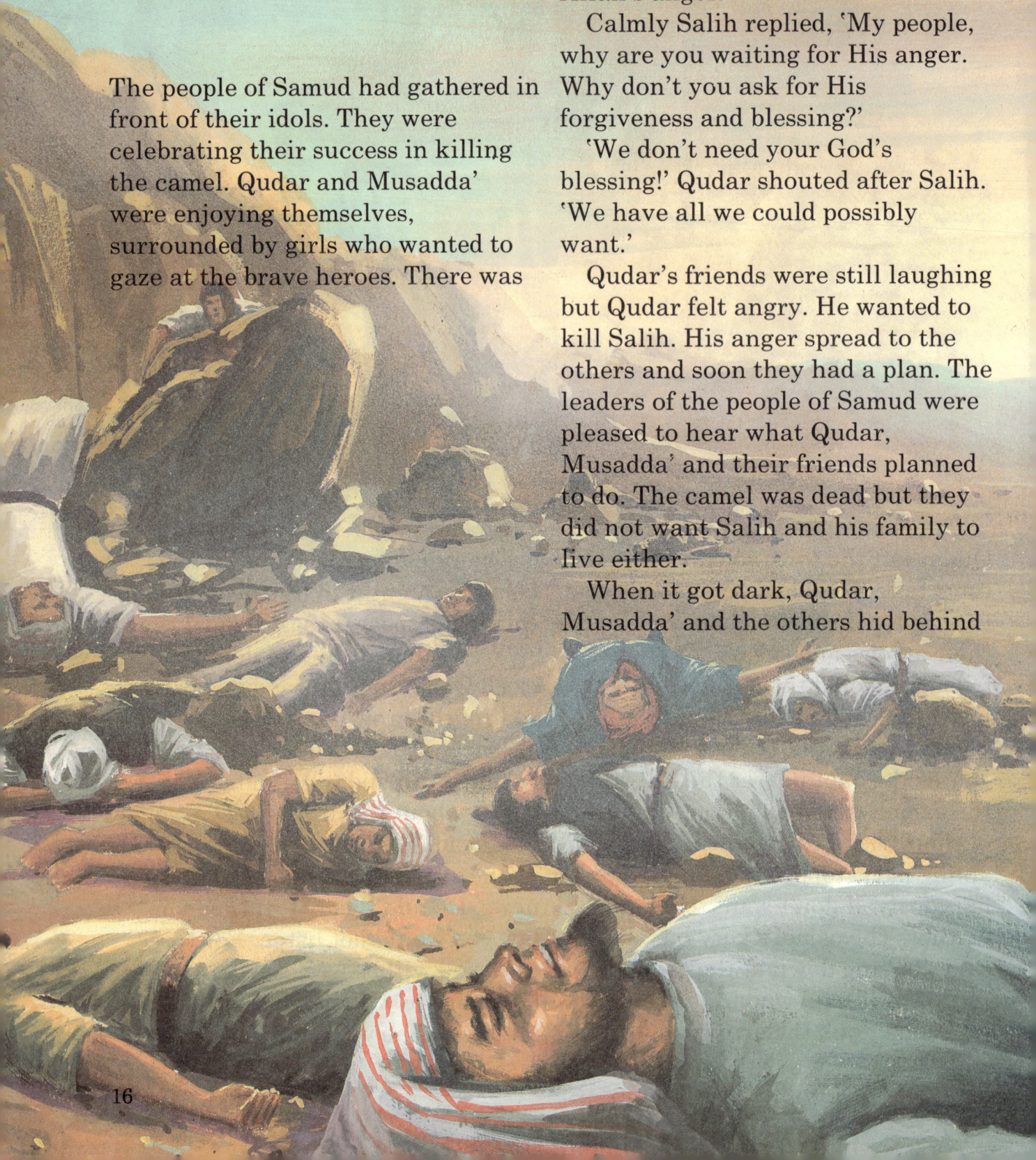

the rocks near the idols. They planned to kill the prophet and his family as they passed by. The night wind began to chill them as they waited. But still the prophet did not come. They did not notice that the wind was getting stronger. Suddenly it blew with such strength that the rocks on the hill moved. The rocks crashed onto the men below and killed them all.

The next morning, 'Unaizah and Sadqah went to look for the men. A crowd of people came with them. They expected to find the prophet Salih and his family dead. They were happy at the thought of greeting their heroes, and laughed as they walked along in the morning sun.

Suddenly the two women at the front stopped. They gazed in horror at the scene before them. The crowd stood in shocked silence behind them, looking at the bodies of Qudar, Musadda' and their friends.

'Perhaps Salih was right', thought 'Unaizah. The prophet's warning rang in her ears. The others were thinking the same as they made their way back home.

Now the people of Samud were frightened. They began to be sorry for what they had done. But it was too late.

Since the killing of the camel, a gentle breeze had been blowing in the valley. But on the third day it became a fierce wind that howled as it blew sand in from the desert. As the frightened people ran to find shelter, they remembered the prophet's words, 'For three days you will be free of Allah's anger, but then He will punish you . . .' The wind and falling rocks destroyed their tents and houses, and drowned the cries of the people. When the wind stopped, there was silence. No one was left alive and sand covered the fertile valley where the people of Samud had lived.

But the prophet Salih and his followers were safe. They had secretly left their homeland, as Allah had told them to, and were making their way to the south of the Arabian Peninsula, to the land of Yaman.

Namrud's dream

King Namrud woke with a start. It was still very early. He sat up, looking very worried. He was thinking. He closed his eyes then opened them again, still thinking.

Azar, King Namrud's bodyguard, noticed that something seemed to be wrong. The faithful Azar never left the King's side. It was Azar's job to protect the King from any harm.

'My lord?', he said, coming closer to the bed. The King looked up but he was still lost in thought.

'Is something worrying you, my lord?' said Azar.

'A dream. I had a dream', said King Namrud. Then he pointed to his crown which lay on a table near the bed. Azar was puzzled.

'Was it a good dream?' he asked. He picked up the crown and gave it to the King.

'No!' said the King angrily. He put the crown on his head then he took it off again.

'This crown', he began, then stopped. He looked at the expensive carpet on the floor, and the beautiful furniture in the room. Then he looked again at the crown in his hands. He was thinking of his dream.

'This crown will be destroyed', he said to himself. But a moment later he sat up straight and said aloud, 'I will never allow that to happen! The dream must be wrong.' He thought of his palace and the country he ruled. It was his palace, the palace of Namrud, King of Babylon. He would never allow anyone to take it from him. He turned to Azar.

'Azar! Go and find the astrologers. Tell them to come to me.'

Azar ran off immediately to obey the King's command. He hurried back with the astrologers. It was still early in the morning but no one dared keep the King waiting.

The astrologers stood trembling before the King in his grand Audience Chamber.

'I want you to tell me what my dream means', said the King. 'I dreamed that a boy came into my room and destroyed my crown.'

Anxiously, the astrologers discussed the dream together. Finally they told the King that one day a boy would be born, and this boy would take the King's place in his palace and in the government of the country.

The King was not pleased. 'What did you say?' he shouted. 'My kingdom will be taken by a boy?'

Together the frightened astrologers said, 'That is our explanation of your dream.' King Namrud sent them away.

The King began to make plans to keep his kingdom safe. He forbade his people to marry. Husbands and wives had to separate. He ordered that no babies were to be born.

No one dared disobey him. Every day a check was made from house to

house. Anyone who was found breaking the King's orders would be killed. The King's orders caused great unhappiness throughout the land, but they had to be obeyed.

Even Azar, the King's bodyguard, had to leave his wife. After some time, Azar's wife was so unhappy at being left on her own that she decided to go to the palace one night to see her husband. She waited until it was very late and all the guards were asleep. Azar was overjoyed to see her. Before it was light, Azar's wife went home again alone, praying that no one would ever find out.

A few weeks later, the astrologers came to see King Namrud. They told him that a woman in the city was pregnant with a baby boy.

King Namrud was furious. He ordered his soldiers to search the city for any pregnant women. All the women were very frightened. Someone might say a woman was pregnant, although it wasn't true, just because they didn't like her.

Azar's wife was more frightened than anyone else. She now knew that she was pregnant. Her husband knew too, but he kept it secret from the King. Night after night, Azar's wife prayed that Allah would protect her unborn child. It was not easy, but she managed to hide her pregnancy. She hardly ever went out of the house. She wore loose clothes. She trusted Allah to help her.

In his palace, King Namrud was frightened, too. His guards had not been able to find any pregnant women in the city. How could the King stop his dream coming true?

One day, Azar saw his wife in secret. She told him the time had almost come for her baby to be born. She was very frightened. Azar was very worried, too. He told his wife there was a cave in the hills outside the city of Babylon. Hardly anyone ever went there. That would be the safest place for her.

Azar's wife made the difficult journey. At every step she prayed to Allah, 'Protect me, protect my child . . .' Finally, she found the cave and went in, making sure no one had seen her.

There her baby was born. She called him Ibrahim.

In the city, the King's guards were searching every house again. The astrologers had just told the King that a baby boy had been born.

In the cave, the mother held her child. 'Protect this child. Save him from harm . . .' she prayed. Carefully, she put him down and left him in Allah's protection. She went back to her home alone.

Allah sent the angel Jibril to look after the child. Jibril held the baby's hand, then put the child's thumb into it's mouth. Milk and honey flowed from the baby's thumb.

The child was safe. Every time his mother went back to the cave to see him, she found him growing bigger and stronger. She gave thanks to Allah.

Ibrahim becomes a prophet

While he was a child, Ibrahim was looked after by the angel Jibril. Ibrahim grew up unharmed because Allah protected him.

In the lonely cave, Ibrahim learned to love the beauty of nature. He watched the wind blow the leaves on the trees and the birds fly across the sky. He watched the sun light up the sky at dawn and the moon and stars twinkle in the sky at night. He had a lot of time to think and questions filled his mind. Who had made the world? Who made day follow night? Who had given life to the birds and the animals – and to him? There was no one to help him

find the answers to these questions.

One day, when Ibrahim was a young man, he left the cave and walked to the city of Babylon. He did not like what he found. His own father made the idols which the people worshipped. Ibrahim could not believe, as they did, that these idols and King Namrud were gods. In his heart Ibrahim knew that a power much greater than King Namrud had made the sun and the moon. He saw poor people suffering while the rich lived in splendid houses and did not need to work. Idols stood everywhere, and crowds of people knelt before them to pray. But how could these idols help the poor?

Ibrahim prayed all the time for a sign from Allah so that he could help his people. At last, his prayers were answered. Allah made Ibrahim His prophet and messenger. Allah sent him a vision: a dream, of the brotherhood of Islam. He taught Ibrahim about the mysteries of the universe and life. Ibrahim's heart was filled with love for Allah, and faith.

Ibrahim thought a lot about the question of life after death. If a man's body had been buried when he died, how could Allah bring him to life again?

Ibrahim left the city again and went to think in the desert. He asked Allah, 'Show me how, on the day of resurrection, You will restore the dead to life.'

Allah replied, 'Have you so little faith, Ibrahim?'

But He told Ibrahim to kill four birds and chop up their bodies into tiny pieces. Ibrahim did as he was told and put the pieces into four little heaps on the hillside. When he told them to become whole again, to his surprise the little heaps turned into bones, flesh and feathers, and four birds flew off into the sky.

'*Masya Allah! Subhanallah!*' gasped Ibrahim. He knelt to worship Allah. He knew Allah could bring men back to life.

'When Allah gives His command, there is no power that can stop Him. Truly Allah is the God of Wisdom and Might.'

The mission of the prophet Ibrahim

That night Ibrahim returned to his house and slept soundly till dawn. In the morning he waited until his father had finished praying to the idols. Then he asked his father, 'Why must you pray to something that you do not hear or see?' (*Al Quran, Surah Maryam, verse 42*)

'These are my gods and the gods of my ancestors', replied his father sternly.

'O Father! Truly it has been revealed to me what has not been revealed to you. Follow me, and I will guide you to the right path.' (*Al Quran, Surah Maryam, verse 43*)

But his father would not listen. 'You want to guide me to the right path! You are still young! Are you cleverer than I am?'

Ibrahim remained calm. 'Do not pray to the devil who was disloyal to Allah.'

He wanted to save his father. 'I am very worried, for you will feel the anger of Allah because you do not pray to Him and you will be the companion of the devil in Hell.' (*Al Quran, Surah Maryam, verse 44–45*)

His father replied, 'Should you hate my gods, Ibrahim? If you do not stop preaching to me and advising me I will stone you. It would be wise for you to take leave of me for ever.' (*Al Quran, Surah Maryam, verse 46*)

Ibrahim was saddened for he loved his father. 'Goodbye, dear father; I will pray to my God that He will forgive your sins; Truly He has bestowed upon me His kindness.' (*Al Quran, Surah Maryam, verse 47*)

Ibrahim was now isolated from his father and from his own people. The people of Babylon liked and respected Ibrahim, but they were surprised when he told them to stop worshipping the idols.

'Can these idols see or hear?' asked Ibrahim. 'They are just stone. How can they help their worshippers? What difference does it make if you stop worshipping them?'

The people were shocked. 'But we have always worshipped the idols', they said. 'Our parents and grandparents worshipped them, and all our people before them, too.'

'They were wrong to do so, and so are you', Ibrahim replied.

This made some of the people angry. 'Are you trying to insult us, Ibrahim?' they asked. 'Or are you just joking?'

The prophet replied calmly. 'I am telling you the truth. I bring you the true religion. I have been sent by Allah to help you find the right path again. The God you should worship is the one who created the Earth and the sky, not these idols or King Namrud.'

The people did not want to listen to Ibrahim. 'We will not accept your God. We will always worship the idols. Why, your own father makes them!'

Ibrahim was silent for a moment, thinking sadly of his father's angry words. But nothing would weaken his faith in Allah. 'My father is like you', he said. 'He is wrong, too.'

The people laughed rudely at Ibrahim. They did not like to hear someone disagree with his own father, or try to change the ancient traditions of the people.

'Use your eyes', pleaded Ibrahim. 'Surely you can see these idols do nothing for you. But Allah watches over me. He has power over life and death.'

People laughed as they walked away and left the prophet alone. But there were some in the crowd who began to believe the prophet's words.

The destruction of the idols

It was nearly time for the annual holiday. In three days time everyone would go to the countryside, leaving only the idols behind to guard the empty city.

Everyone was busy getting ready for the celebrations. Some people had made cakes, others had killed goats to eat. Before they left, they put offerings at the feet of the idols who would protect the city while they were away.

On the first day of the holiday everyone got up very early. Their laughter could be heard for miles around as they made their way into the countryside. The dawn sky grew brighter as the sun rose higher. The people were looking forward to several days of singing and dancing, eating and drinking, with the men, women and children all together.

There was one man left in the city. He had not gone with the others. He had plans of his own.

He left his house, carrying an axe firmly in one hand. He walked quickly towards the house of worship. He was going to destroy the idols. He had thought about what he was going to do for a long time. He realised that the people needed proof that the idols they worshipped had no power, that they were just pieces of stone.

'I'll show them, and then they will believe the words of Allah', thought the prophet as he walked along.

No one saw him go into the house of worship. Only the idols were there and their eyes could not see. Ibrahim laughed when he saw the food the people had left for the idols.

'Why don't you eat it?' he said aloud, looking up at the huge stone statues. 'How can they worship these lifeless stones?' he thought as he swung his axe through the air.

Ibrahim swung the axe again and again, and soon the idols lay broken and scattered on the ground. Just one was left – the largest. The prophet walked up to it and hung the axe round its neck. 'When your worshippers come and ask, you can tell them who did it', said Ibrahim aloud, smiling. Then he left the house of worship.

After a few days, the people began to return to the city. They had thought of nothing but their own pleasures while they were away, so the first thing they did was to go to the house of worship to bow to their idols.

They were shocked to see the statues lying in ruins. 'Who has committed this crime?' they asked themselves. The people wept at the sight of their broken idols and cried, 'Our gods are dead!'

'We will find the man who has done this!' cried one group of men.

'We will kill him when we find him!' shouted others.

'I think this is the work of Ibrahim', said a voice from the crowd.

'Ibrahim?'

'Yes, Ibrahim, the young man who is always telling us to stop worshipping our gods.'

'Come on, let's find him', agreed the crowd.

Ibrahim did not hide. He wanted to talk to the people. He stood there calmly as the crowd shouted angrily at him.

'Are you the one who destroyed our gods?' asked one of the leaders.

Ibrahim pointed to the large statue that was still standing. 'That statue was angry', he said. 'He destroyed the rest of your idols.

Look, there is the axe round his neck. Why don't you ask him instead of me?'

'Why do you tell us to ask an idol? He can't speak', said the leader, falling straight into the prophet's trap.

'If that is so, why do you worship these idols? They are statues which cannot talk, cannot see, cannot hear. They can't even save themselves from destruction. What can they do for you?' the prophet asked. 'How can you be stupid enough to believe in them and worship them? Don't you see that what you are doing is wrong? Why don't you worship Allah who made the world and everything you see around you?'

The people were silent. They had no answer.

Faith tested by fire

The prophet's words soon reached the ears of Namrud himself. The prophet could not be ignored. He had destroyed the idols and claimed that Allah was the One True God. This was too much for King Namrud, who imagined himself to be a god.

'There is only one punishment dreadful enough to match what Ibrahim has done', declared the King. 'And that is death by fire.'

The ministers, the priests and most of the people agreed with him.

'We will burn Ibrahim!' they shouted. They were delighted at the thought of punishing him.

The prophet was not frightened. He was ready to accept anything that happened to him. He put his life in the hands of Allah.

Ibrahim stood before King Namrud.

'Ibrahim, do you not fear the fire?' asked the King, hoping to see the prophet tremble.

'Fire, too, was made by Allah', replied the prophet. 'If it burns, it is Allah's will. I put my life and my soul in the hands of Allah.'

'Burn him!' cried the crowd.

Each man brought a bundle of firewood and these were made into a large heap in the middle of a field.

Crowds came to watch the burning. King Namrud came, too. It was his right to light the fire.

Ibrahim's few faithful followers stood sadly to one side, praying to Allah. There was nothing else they could do. There were too few of them and they were too weak. 'Oh Allah, save the prophet Ibrahim', they prayed. 'Save Your religion.'

King Namrud lit the fire. The flames leapt up from the dry wood into the sky. No one could get near the fire, it was so hot. Even birds flying over it were burnt to ashes. King Namrud looked at the fire with pleasure, then he turned to the prophet. Everyone was surprised to see the prophet looking so calm. He might have been standing under a shady tree instead of beside a burning furnace. He did not seem to feel the heat. He stood still and repeated the name of Allah endlessly.

King Namrud ordered his guards to throw the prophet into the fire. It was too hot for anyone to go near, so they put the prophet into a sling that would hurl him into the fire like an arrow from a bow.

All the King's guards helped to pull the sling back, except Azar, Ibrahim's father. He could not bear to see his son thrown into the flames.

Then the King gave the order and the prophet was hurled into the fire.

A cry rose from the crowd and some fled because they could not bear the sight.

But Allah would not let His prophet be hurt. He sent a command:

'Oh fire, be cool,
save My servant, Ibrahim.'
(*Al Quran, Surah al-Anbiya, verse 69*)

And the fire began to die. The flames were replaced by clouds of black smoke, the blazing fire became a glow, and the glow became ashes.

The prophet was untouched. He stood alone in the middle of the ashes that were all that was left of the great fire. Only the ropes that had been round his hands and feet had been burnt. Calmly, he walked out of the ashes. The people were

They gave thanks to Allah.

Many people accepted the way of Allah from that day. The miracle was all the proof they needed that Ibrahim had been telling the truth.

Namrud became even more worried. He sent for Ibrahim and told him to stop telling the people that he, Namrud, was not their god. But the prophet replied, 'Allah is greater than any man alive or dead'.

Ibrahim would not stop spreading his faith and soon he was forced to leave his homeland.

speechless. The King said nothing. He bit his lip and shook his head in amazement. He turned and left the field. The people returned home in silence. The faithful followers ran up to Ibrahim crying, 'Ibrahim is safe!'